GARFIELD

I Am What I Am!

JIM DAVIS

ЯR
RAVETTE PUBLISHING

© 2005 PAWS, INCORPORATED
All rights reserved.

"GARFIELD" and the GARFIELD characters
are registered and unregistered trademarks
of Paws, Incorporated.

(www.garfield.com)

First published by Ravette Publishing 2005.

This book is sold subject to the condition that
it shall not, by way of trade or otherwise, be
lent, resold, hired out or otherwise circulated
without the publisher's prior consent in any
form of binding or cover other than that in
which it is published and without a similar
condition including this condition being
imposed on the subsequent purchaser.

Printed and bound in Great Britain
for Ravette Publishing Limited,
Unit 3, Tristar Centre,
Star Road, Partridge Green,
West Sussex RH13 8RA

by Cox & Wyman, Reading, Berkshire.

ISBN: 1 84161 243 X

www.garfield.com

Distributed by Universal Press Syndicate

© 2001 PAWS, INC. All Rights Reserved

www.garfield.com

Distributed by Universal Press Syndicate

JiM DAViS 8-1

© 2001 PAWS, INC All Rights Reserved

♪FEEELINGS...

WHAT IS A KARAOKE MACHINE DOING IN THE LIVING ROOM?

© 2001 PAWS, INC. All Rights Reserved

© 2001 PAWS, INC. All Rights Reserved

www.garfield.com
Distributed by Universal Press Syndicate
© 2001 PAWS, INC. All Rights Reserved

www.garfield.com

Distributed by Universal Press Syndicate

© 2001 PAWS, INC All Rights Reserved

www.garfield.com

Distributed by Universal Press Syndicate

© 2001 PAWS, INC. All Rights Reserved

www.garfield.com

Distributed by Universal Press Syndicate

© 2001 PAWS, INC. All Rights Reserved

JIM DAVIS 10-22

WHOOOOMP!

BUNGEE DOGGGG!

www.garfield.com

JIM DAVIS 10-25

Distributed by Universal Press Syndicate

© 2001 PAWS, INC. All Rights Reserved

www.garfield.com

Distributed by Universal Press Syndicate

© 2001 PAWS, INC. All Rights Reserved

© 2001 PAWS, INC. All rights Reserved

JIM DAVIS 11-14

www.garfield.com

Distributed by Universal Press Syndicate

GARFIELD, YOU OAF! THAT WAS MY FOOT YOU STEPPED ON!

GAAAHH

NOW YOU HAVE A MATCHED SET

www.garfield.com

Distributed by Universal Press Syndicate

© 2001 PAWS, INC. All Rights Reserved

www.garfield.com

Distributed by Universal Press Syndicate

www.garfield.com

Distributed by Universal Press Syndicate

SLUURRP!

AAAGGHH

© 2001 PAWS, INC. All Rights Reserved

EWW...WHAT IS HE DOING?

WRINGING OUT HIS BEARD

VISIT SANTA →

JIM DAVIS 12-8

OTHER GARFIELD BOOKS AVAILABLE

Pocket Books	Price	ISBN
Below Par	£3.50	1 84161 152 2
Compute This!	£3.50	1 84161 194 8
Double Trouble	£3.50	1 84161 008 9
Eat My Dust	£3.99	1 84161 098 4
Fun in the Sun	£3.99	1 84161 097 6
Goooooooal!	£3.99	1 84161 037 2
Gotcha!	£3.50	1 84161 226 X
I Don't Do Perky	£3.50	1 84161 195 6
Light Of My Life	£3.50	1 85304 353 2
Pop Star	£3.50	1 84161 151 4
S.W.A.L.K.	£3.50	1 84161 225 1
To Eat, Or Not To Eat?	£3.50	1 85304 991 3

New title available Feb 2006

No.51 - Feed Me!	£3.99	1 84161 242 1

Theme Books		
Behaving Badly	£4.50	1 85304 892 5
Cat Napping	£4.50	1 84161 087 9
Coffee Mornings	£4.50	1 84161 086 0
Creatures Great & Small	£3.99	1 85304 998 0
Entertains You	£4.50	1 84161 221 9
Healthy Living	£3.99	1 85304 972 7
Pigging Out	£4.50	1 85304 893 3
Slam Dunk!	£4.50	1 84161 222 7
Successful Living	£3.99	1 85304 973 5
The Seasons	£3.99	1 85304 999 9

2-in-1 Theme Books		
All In Good Taste	£6.99	1 84161 209 X
Easy Does It	£6.99	1 84161 191 3
Lazy Daze	£6.99	1 84161 208 1
Licensed to Thrill	£6.99	1 84161 192 1
Out For The Couch	£6.99	1 84161 144 1
The Gruesome Twosome	£6.99	1 84161 143 3

Classics		Price	ISBN
Volume One		£5.99	1 85304 970 0
Volume Two		£5.99	1 85304 971 9
Volume Three		£5.99	1 85304 996 4
Volume Four		£5.99	1 85304 997 2
Volume Five		£5.99	1 84161 022 4
Volume Six		£5.99	1 84161 023 2
Volume Seven		£5.99	1 84161 088 7
Volume Eight		£5.99	1 84161 089 5
Volume Nine		£5.99	1 84161 149 2
Volume Ten		£5.99	1 84161 150 6
Volume Eleven		£5.99	1 84161 175 1
Volume Twelve		£5.99	1 84161 176 X
Volume Thirteen		£5.99	1 84161 206 5
Volume Fourteen		£5.99	1 84161 207 3
Volume Fifteen	(new)	£5.99	1 84161 232 4
Volume Sixteen	(new)	£5.99	1 84161 233 2
Little Books			
C-c-c-caffeine		£2.50	1 84161 183 2
Food 'n' Fitness		£2.50	1 84161 145 X
Laughs		£2.50	1 84161 146 8
Love 'n' Stuff		£2.50	1 84161 147 6
Surf 'n' Sun		£2.50	1 84161 186 7
The Office		£2.50	1 84161 184 0
Zzzzzzz		£2.50	1 84161 185 9
Miscellaneous			
Garfield the Movie		£7.99	1 84161 205 7
Garfield 25 years of me!		£7.99	1 84161 173 5
Treasury 6	(new)	£10.99	1 84161 229 4
Treasury 5		£10.99	1 84161 198 0
Treasury 4		£10.99	1 84161 180 8
Treasury 3		£9.99	1 84161 142 5

All Garfield books are available at your local bookshop or from the publisher at the address below. Just tick the titles required and send the form with your payment to:-

RAVETTE PUBLISHING
Unit 3, Tristar Centre, Star Road, Partridge Green, West Sussex RH13 8RA

Prices and availability are subject to change without notice.
Please enclose a cheque or postal order made payable to **Ravette Publishing** to the value of the cover price of the book and allow the following for UK postage and packing:

60p for the first book + 30p for each additional book
except *Garfield Treasuries* when please add £3.00 per copy for p&p

Name ....

Address ....

....

....